PLANNING AND MANAGING OF WATER RESOURCES

PLANNING AND MANAGING OF WATER RESOURCES

PETER A. UNWAL
EDITOR

Novinka Books
An imprint of Nova Science Publishers, Inc.
New York

For permission to use material from this book please contact us:
Telephone 631-231-7269; Fax 631-231-8175
Web Site: http://www.novapublishers.com

Library of Congress Cataloging-in-Publication Data:
Available Upon Request

ISBN: 1-59454-757-2

Published by Nova Science Publishers, Inc. ✢ New York

CONTENTS

Preface		**vii**
Chapter 1	**Western Water Resource Issues** *Betsy A. Cody and Pervaze A. Sheikh*	**1**
Chapter 2	**Upper Mississippi River System: Proposals to Restore an Inland Waterway's Ecosystem** *Kyna Powers and Nicole T. Carter*	**23**
Index		**49**

PREFACE

For more than a century, the federal government has constructed water resource projects for a variety of purposes, including flood control, navigation, power generation, and irrigation. While most municipal and industrial water supplies have been built by non-federal entities, most of the large, federal water supply projects in the West, including Hoover and Grand Coulee dams, were constructed by the Bureau of Reclamation (Department of the Interior) to provide water for irrigation. Growing populations and changing values have increased demands on water supplies and river systems, resulting in water use and management conflicts throughout the country, particularly in the West, where the population is expected to increase 30% in the next 20-25 years. In many western states, agricultural needs are often in direct conflict with urban needs, as well as with water demand for threatened and endangered species, recreation, and scenic enjoyment. Debate over western water resources revolves around the issue of how best to plan for and manage the use of this renewable, yet sometimes scarce and increasingly sought after, resource. Some observers advocate enhancing water supplies, for example, by building new storage or diversion projects, expanding old ones, or funding water reclamation and reuse facilities. Others emphasize the need to manage existing supplies more efficiently through conservation, revision of policies that encourage inefficient use of water, and establishment of market mechanisms to allocate water. Recent proposals to expand the Upper Mississippi River-Illinois Waterway (UMR-IWW) a major transportation route for products moving to and from Illinois, Iowa, Minnesota, Missouri, and Wisconsin have met with significant controversy. Some of this controversy centers on the cumulative environmental effects of the current navigation system and the proposed expansion. The Upper Mississippi River System (UMRS), which includes the navigation channel and surrounding floodplain supports an unusually large number of species for a temperate river. The UMR-IWW navigation system alters UMRS habitat and contributes to a decline in the abundance of some species. For example, locks, dams, and other channel structures inhibit the movement of fish between and within river segments; fill side channels, backwaters, and wetlands with sediment; and suppress plant growth by reducing water clarity.

In: Planning and Managing of Water Resources ISBN 1-59454-757-2
Editor: Peter A. Unwal, pp. 1-21

Chapter 1

WESTERN WATER RESOURCE ISSUES*

Betsy A. Cody and Pervaze A. Sheikh

SUMMARY

For more than a century, the federal government has constructed water resource projects for a variety of purposes, including flood control, navigation, power generation, and irrigation. While most municipal and industrial water supplies have been built by non-federal entities, most of the large, federal water supply projects in the West, including Hoover and Grand Coulee dams, were constructed by the Bureau of Reclamation (Department of the Interior) to provide water for irrigation.

Growing populations and changing values have increased demands on water supplies and river systems, resulting in water use and management conflicts throughout the country, particularly in the West, where the population is expected to increase 30% in the next 20-25 years. In many western states, agricultural needs are often in direct conflict with urban needs, as well as with water demand for threatened and endangered species, recreation, and scenic enjoyment.

Debate over western water resources revolves around the issue of how best to plan for and manage the use of this renewable, yet sometimes scarce and increasingly sought after, resource. Some observers advocate enhancing water supplies, for example, by building new

* Excerpted from CRS Report IB10019, dated May 19, 2005.

storage or diversion projects, expanding old ones, or funding water reclamation and reuse facilities. Others emphasize the need to manage existing supplies more efficiently — through conservation, revision of policies that encourage inefficient use of water, and establishment of market mechanisms to allocate water.

The 109th Congress is likely to consider a number of bills on western water issues, including title transfer, water recycling, and rural water supply legislation and may also revisit drought legislation introduced in the 108th Congress. Oversight of CALFED — a joint federal and state program to restore fish and wildlife habitat and address California water supply/quality issues — and Klamath River Basin issues is also likely.

The 109th Congress may also consider Indian water rights settlement legislation; however, Indian settlement bills are not tracked in this issue brief.

Most Recent Developments

On May 11, 2005, the Senate Energy and Natural Resources Committee held a hearing on S. 895, a bill to establish a new rural water supply program to be administered by the Bureau of in Reclamation, Department of the Interior. The bill combines elements of three bills that had been introduced in the 108th Congress: S. 1085 (Bingaman), S. 1732 (Domenici, by request), and S. 2218 (Domenici).

Recent news reports of food chain and fisheries declines in the Sacramento and San Joaquin Rivers confluence with San Francisco Bay (Bay-Delta), combined with fiscal issues at both the state and federal levels, have raised questions about the implementation and viability of the CALFED Program — a federal and state effort to coordinate water management and ecosystem restoration activities within and around the Bay-Delta. The Administration's FY2006 request for the Bureau of Reclamation's CALFED program account is $35 million; the House Appropriations Committee approved that amount during full committee markup of FY2006 Energy and Water Development legislation (H.R. 2419) on May 18, 2005.

To date, ten Title 16 (water re-use and recycling) bills have been introduced in the 109th Congress (two bills are identical). Numerous other water supply, conservation, and western water bills have also been introduced.

In pending legislation, S. 728, the Water Resources Development Act of 2005, the U.S. Army Corps of Engineers would be authorized to conduct a study of pilot projects identified in the preferred restoration concept plan approved by the Salton Sea Authority. This study would determine that the pilot projects are economically justifiable, technically sound, environmentally acceptable, and meet the objectives of restoring the Salton Sea. Under S. 728, a total cost of $26.0 million would be authorized, of which $16.9 million would be the federal cost, and $9.1 million the non-federal cost.

BACKGROUND AND ANALYSIS

For more than a century, the federal government has been involved in developing water projects for a variety of purposes, including flood control, navigation, power generation, and irrigation. Most major water projects, such as large dams and diversions, were constructed by either the Bureau of Reclamation (Bureau), in the Department of the Interior, or the U.S. Army Corps of Engineers (Corps), in the Department of Defense. Traditionally, the Corps has built and maintained projects designed primarily for flood control, navigation, and power generation, whereas Bureau projects were designed primarily to facilitate settlement of the West by storing and providing reliable supplies of water for irrigation and "reclamation" of arid lands. While both agencies supply water for some municipal and industrial uses, they do so largely as a secondary responsibility in connection with larger multipurpose projects. Most of the nation's public municipal water systems have been built by local communities under prevailing state water laws.

Today, the Bureau operates nearly 350 storage reservoirs and approximately 250 diversion dams — including some of the largest dams in the world, such as Hoover Dam on the Colorado River and Grand Coulee Dam on the Columbia River. In total, the Bureau's projects provide water to approximately 9 million acres of farmland and nearly 31 million people in 17 western states. The Bureau also operates 58 power plants. Because of the strategic importance of its largest facilities, the Bureau has heightened security at all key facilities to protect projects in the wake of the terrorist attacks on September 11, 2001.

Most Bureau water supply projects were built under authority granted to the Secretary of the Interior in the Reclamation Act of 1902, or through individual project authorizations. The original intent of the Reclamation Act was to encourage families to settle and farm lands in the arid and semi-arid West, where precipitation is typically 30% to 50% of what it is in the East. Construction of reclamation projects expanded greatly during the 1930s and 1940s, and continued rapidly until the late 1960s and early 1970s. By the late 1960s, a combination of changing national priorities and local needs, increasing construction costs, and the prior development of most prime locations for water works contributed to a decline in new construction of major water works nationwide. Water supply for traditional off-stream uses — including municipal, industrial, and agricultural uses — was increasingly in direct competition with a growing interest in allocating water to maintain or enhance in-stream uses, such as recreation, scenic enjoyment, and fisheries and wildlife habitat.

During the 1970s, construction of new projects slowed to a handful of major works, culminating in the completion of the Tellico dam project in Tennessee and the Tennessee Tombigbee waterway through Alabama and Mississippi. These projects pitted conservation and environmental groups, as well as some fiscal conservatives, against the traditional water resources development community. New on the scene was the National Environmental Policy Act of 1970 (NEPA), which for the first time required an assessment of the environmental effects of federal projects, and provided for more public scrutiny of such projects. In 1978, President Carter announced that future federal water policy would focus on improving water resources management, constructing only projects that were economically viable, cooperating with state and local entities, and sustaining environmental quality. The Reagan Administration continued to oppose large projects, contending they were fiscally unsound. New construction of federally financed water projects virtually stopped until Congress passed the Water Resources Development Act (WRDA) of 1986, which addressed Corps projects and policies. Federal water research and planning activities were also reduced during the early years of the Reagan Administration, which felt that states should have a greater role in carrying out such activities. Consistent with this outlook, President Reagan abolished the Water Resources Council, an umbrella agency established in 1968 to coordinate federal water policy and to assess the status of the nation's water resource and development needs.

Congress subsequently scaled back several remaining authorized projects, changed repayment and cost-share structures, and passed laws that altered project operations and water delivery programs. For example, in 1982 Congress passed the Reclamation Reform Act, which altered the Bureau's water pricing policies for some users. The act revised acreage limitation requirements and charges for water received to irrigate leased lands. Congress soon increased local entities' share in construction costs for Corps water resource projects with passage of the 1986 WRDA.

Over the last decade, both the Corps and the Bureau have undertaken projects or programs aimed at mitigating or preventing environmental degradation due in part to the construction and operation of large water projects, while at the same time expanding water supply facilities. The agencies have pursued these actions through administrative efforts and congressional mandates, as well as in response to court actions. Currently, the federal government is involved in several restoration initiatives including the Florida Everglades, the California Bay-Delta, and the Columbia and Snake River basins in the Pacific Northwest. These initiatives have been quite controversial. Each involves many stakeholders at the local and regional level (water users, landowners, farmers, commercial and sports fishermen, urban water suppliers and users, navigational interests, hydropower customers and providers, recreationists, and environmentalists) and has been years in the making. At the same time, demand for traditional or new water resource projects continues — particularly for ways to augment local water supplies, maintain or improve navigation, and control or prevent floods and shoreline erosion. In addition, demand continues from some sectors for new or previously authorized large water supply projects (e.g., Auburn and Temperance Flats dams, and Sites Reservoir in California). For both the Everglades and CALFED, water supply facilities are included in proposals for restoration.

LEGISLATIVE AND OVERSIGHT ISSUES

The 109th Congress is likely to consider several water resource issues in legislation ranging from transferring title of federal facilities to local project users, to individual project authorizations and agency policy changes (e.g., reoperation of water project facilities in the Central Valley of California and in the Colorado and Columbia River Basins). Oversight of ongoing agency activities, such as water management in the Klamath River Basin, Salton Sea restoration, allocation of Colorado River water supplies (particularly within California), and authorization of a program to carry out activities affecting the delta confluence of the San Joaquin and Sacramento Rivers at the San Francisco Bay (Bay-Delta, or CALFED) may also be discussed. The broader topic of whether to review federal water activities or establish a national water policy commission was discussed during the 108th Congress, and may also be addressed in the 109th. Funding and policy direction through the annual Energy and Water appropriations bill also influences the construction and operation of projects. (See CRS Report RL32852, *Appropriations for FY2006: Energy and Water Development.*) In particular, appropriations language concerning funding (or lack thereof) for the CALFED program has been the subject of much debate.

Security of Reclamation Facilities

Security remains heightened at Bureau facilities in the wake of terrorist attacks in New York and Washington D.C. on September 11, 2001. The Bureau initially closed visitor facilities and cancelled tours at all facilities. While most visitor facilities have reopened, facilities may close or reopen depending on security alert levels and site-specific concerns at any time. For example, the Bureau heightened security at many facilities during recent code orange alerts and is expected to do so in the future. Further, in February 2004, the Bureau closed the road over Folsom Dam (CA), largely because of security concerns. Legislation to authorize the Bureau to build a new bridge near the dam has been introduced (H.R. 901). The Administration opposes the legislation largely on the grounds of its cost — $66 million (roughly 8% of the Bureau's annual budget).

Because Bureau facilities were not directly affected by September 11 events, it did not receive funding in the first two releases of emergency supplemental appropriations following the attack. However, the agency received $30.3 million for security at Bureau facilities as part of the third cluster of emergency supplemental funding included in Division B, Chapter 5, of the FY2002 Defense Appropriations bill (H.R. 3338, P.L. 107-117). The Bureau received $28.6 million for site security for FY2004 and $43.2 million in FY2005. For FY2006, the Administration has requested $50.0 million for site security. The House Appropriations Committee on May 18 approved $40 million in appropriations and the collection of $10 million from water users for security operations costs, for a total of $50 million for the program.

Klamath River Basin

The Klamath River Basin — an area on the California-Oregon border — has become a focal point for local and national discussions on water management and water scarcity. These issues were brought to the forefront in 2001 when severe drought prompted the Bureau to curtail irrigation water deliveries to approximately 200,000 acres of farm and pasture lands within the roughly 235,000-acre Klamath Project service area. The cutback was made to make water available for three fish species under federal Endangered Species Act (ESA) protection (two endangered sucker species, and a threatened coho salmon population). Tensions were also high in 2002 when water temperatures and atypically low flows in the lower Klamath corresponded with the death of at least 33,000 adult salmon.

The Klamath Project has been part of increasingly complex water management issues involving several tribes, fishermen, farmers, environmentalists, hydropower producers, and recreationists. Upstream farmers are generally pitted against fishermen, Native American interests, and other downstream users, and many sides have policy concerns involving valuable sectors of the local economy. Farmers point to their contractual rights to water deliveries from the federal Klamath Project and to hardships for their families if water is cut off; others assert that the salmon fishery is also economically valuable and that farmers could be provided temporary economic assistance, while salmon extinction would be permanent. Still others assert that there are ways to serve all interests, or that the science underlying the determinations of the relevant agencies is simply wrong.

One specific issue is how to operate the Bureau's project facilities to meet irrigation contract obligations without jeopardizing the three listed fish. To address this issue, the Bureau issued a 10-year operations plan in February 2002 and a biological assessment (necessary under the ESA) for operating its Klamath Project. However, subsequent biological opinions found the Bureau's 10-year operations plan would likely jeopardize the continued existence of the listed suckers and coho salmon, as well as adversely modify proposed critical habitat. Although biological opinions issued on May 31, 2002, by the U.S. Fish and Wildlife Service (FWS) and the National Marine Fisheries Service (now called NOAA Fisheries) both included "reasonable and prudent alternatives," the Bureau formally rejected both final biological opinions and opted to operate under a one-year plan that it asserts complies with the opinions. While met with enthusiasm from area farmers, the Bureau's decision drew much criticism and concern from environmentalists, fishermen, tribes, and others. On April 10, 2003, the Bureau issued its Klamath Project 2003 operations plan and noted that planning for multiyear operations of the project is ongoing; the Bureau is expected to issue its 2005 operating plan in April 2005. In both 2003 and 2004, the Bureau stated that the current year plan was consistent with the

2002 biological opinions. The ESA agencies (FWS and NOAA Fisheries) have not issued a biological opinion on the one-year operations plans and instead are working within the biological opinions released in May 2002.

Because of the controversy in 2001, the Secretary of the Interior asked the National Research Council (NRC) to evaluate the federal biological opinions that had been used to prevent the Bureau from delivering water to farmers in 2001. The NRC released an interim report in February 2002 and a final report in October 2003; both concluded there was neither sound scientific basis for maintaining Upper Klamath Lake levels and increased river flows as recommended in the 2001 biological opinions, nor sufficient basis for supporting the lower flows in the Bureau's original operations plan for 2001. Further, the NRC concluded that recovery of endangered suckers and threatened coho salmon in the Klamath Basin might best be achieved by broadly addressing land and water management concerns (including the Klamath dams). NRC also concluded that operation of the Klamath Project (as opposed to operation of other basin projects such as that on the Trinity River) was not the cause of a 2002 lower basin fish kill, and changes in Klamath project operations would not have prevented the fish kill. On October 13, 2004, the Secretary of the Interior announced the signing of a Klamath Watershed Coordination Agreement among four cabinet-level federal agencies. The agreement was initiated to address the fractured resource management specifically noted by the NRC and others.

Legislation pertaining to the Klamath Basin has not been proposed in the 109th Congress. However, the 108th Congress passed §132 of P.L. 108-137, the Energy and Water Development Appropriations for 2004. This section provides authority for the Secretary of the Army to provide "environmental assistance" (design and construction assistance to improve water use efficiency) to non-federal interests in the Upper Klamath River Basin. Additional funding for Klamath basin activities is likely to be included in FY2006 appropriations.

Title Transfer

Congress more and more is considering legislation that would transfer the ownership (title) of individual Bureau of Reclamation water supply projects to current water users. These "title transfer" bills vary depending on the circumstances of each project; however, some general issues apply. Transfer issues range from questions regarding a project's worth and valuation to legal and policy questions regarding the transfer's affect on other area water users, fish and wildlife, future project operations, and future management of lands associated with the project.

The Administration first actively negotiated title transfer on a voluntary basis with interested water/irrigation districts beginning in 1995 when it announced a policy "framework" to establish a process for negotiating title transfers. While some districts pursued the Administration's framework process, others sought direct legislative authority for transfers. In general, Congress must authorize transfer of title to reclamation facilities (32 Stat. 389; 43 U.S.C. 498), regardless of the process used to get to a transfer agreement.

A central issue with title transfer legislation is whether the transfers should be mandated or just authorized. Some argue that the transfers are "minor land transactions" and advocate that Congress direct they take place within a certain time period. Others strongly disagree. Debate mostly centers on the role the National Environmental Policy Act (NEPA) would and should play prior to a project's transfer. Environmentalists generally fear that a directed transfer with or without specific NEPA language would effectively allow the Bureau and project transfer proponents to avoid assessing and/or mitigating environmental effects of the proposed transfers. Conversely, project proponents have pursued directed transfers to avoid what they see as unnecessary delays and to ensure transfers take place. For example, some title transfer legislation directs the transfer to occur "in accordance with all applicable law," while other legislation directs it to take place pursuant to an agreement already negotiated with project water users. Some laws authorize the transfers (e.g., P.L. 106-220 and P.L. 106-221), whereas others direct the transfer (e.g., P.L. 106-249, P.L. 106-377, and P.L. 106-512).

Other discussions center on the role the Endangered Species Act (ESA) might play on project operations after the transfer. One of the main concerns for environmentalists appears to be that once the project is out of federal ownership there will no longer be a legal obligation for the district to consult with other federal entities on the impact of project operations on threatened or endangered species, as is now required of the Bureau under Section 7 of the ESA. Additionally, environmentalists and others fear that once out of federal hands there will be little if any public scrutiny of project operations. Conversely, project proponents are likely to favor private operations.

Controversies regarding the application of NEPA and ESA to project title transfers, as well as the question of whether to direct or authorize the transfers, are likely to remain at issue. Other issues involve concerns about the overall costs of the transfers, who should pay for costs associated with the transfer, effects on third parties, liability, the valuation of project facilities and lands (and treatment of mineral or other receipts), and financial compensation for the projects. Related to many of the issues outlined above is the question of how these projects might be operated in the future. Although the House Resources Committee has noted that it contemplates that facilities would be maintained and managed without significant changes, and in some cases bill language states that the projects shall be managed for the purposes for which the project was authorized, transfer bills approved by the committees have been silent on enforcement issues and in describing what might occur if the new owners change operations (other than they must comply with all applicable laws at that time). Little has been said, for example, about what might occur if new project owners decided to partition project lands for new homes and convert irrigation water to domestic use.

In total, four title transfers were approved during the 108th Congress (two in P.L. 108-382, and one each in P.L. 108-315 and P.L. 108-85, which passed during the first session). To date, no title transfer legislation has been introduced in the 109th Congress.

Project Construction

California Bay-Delta/CALFED

On October 25, 2004, the President signed into law P.L. 108-361 (H.R. 2828), a bill to authorize implementation of the CALFED Bay-Delta Program. Authorization for federal funding for the CALFED Program expired at the end of FY2000, although some activities supporting the program were funded. P.L. 108-361 authorizes $389 million for the federal share of costs for activities authorized under the act for FY2005-FY2010. The Administration's FY2006 request for the Bureau of Reclamation's CALFED program account is $35 million; the House Appropriations Committee approved that amount during full committee markup of H.R. 2419 on May 18.

The authorization of an annual appropriation of $143 million for implementing portions of an ecosystem protection plan and long-term restoration projects for the San Francisco Bay/San Joaquin and Sacramento Rivers Delta (Bay-Delta, also known as the CALFED program) expired September 30, 2000. The initial authorization for CALFED funding (P.L. 104-208, Division E) came on the heels of a 1994 agreement among state and federal agencies, urban, agricultural, and environmental interests to protect the Bay-Delta while satisfying key needs of various involved interests. A Record of Decision (ROD) for the current CALFED Program was issued by a consortium of state and federal agencies in August 2000. The process was initiated to address critical water quality, water supply, and fish and wildlife habitat issues in the 738,000 acre Bay-Delta estuary and has grown into a comprehensive effort to address long-term water supply/quality issues for most of the state.

On October 25, 2004, the President signed into law P.L. 108-361 (H.R. 2828) — a bill to authorize implementation of the CALFED Bay-Delta Program. P.L. 108-361 approves the ROD as a framework for addressing the CALFED Bay-Delta Program and authorizes, under existing and new authorizations, several activities and projects related to the components of CALFED. This law also authorizes $389 million for the federal share of costs for activities authorized under the act for FY2005-FY2010. For more information on the status of the CALFED Program, see CRS Report RL31975, *CALFED Bay-Delta Program: Overview of Institutional and Water Use Issues*, by Pervaze A. Sheikh and Betsy A. Cody.

The debate over the reauthorization of CALFED in the 108th Congress largely centered on specific issues such as authorization for water storage projects, cost allocation, balance among project and program activities, and water supplies for the environment, as well as broader issues such as governance and the degree to which the ROD is implemented. The chief difference between the two reported bills was how they addressed water storage project authorization. The House bill would have "pre-authorized" construction of storage projects based on feasibility studies that adhere to requirements provided in the bill, and subject to a congressional disapproval resolution. The Senate bill took a very different approach and instead set a timeline for Congress to consider the authorization of storage projects listed in the bill. If a storage project is not authorized under the Senate bill within the specified timeline, an "imbalance determination" is triggered, which forces a rebalancing process and reconsideration of the project (and alternatives) by Congress.

In general, storage proponents have voiced concern that environmental aspects of the program have outpaced progress on developing new water supplies. On the other hand, some environmental groups and others have vocally opposed storage language such as the "pre-authorization" language. Some also believed granting authorization (subject to a disapproval resolution) prior to completion of project feasibility studies would amount to a forfeiture of congressional authority over final projects and that the Senate would again reject a bill with "pre-authorization" language. Ultimately, lawmakers decided to approve the Senate-passed version of H.R. 2828.

Oversight issues during the 109th Congress are expected to include project financing, water storage project programs, and implementation of the Operations Criteria and Plan and South Delta Improvements Plan. However, recent news reports of food chain and fisheries declines in the Sacramento and San Joaquin Rivers confluence with San Francisco Bay (Bay-Delta), combined with fiscal issues at both the state and federal levels, have raised questions about the implementation and viability of the CALFED Program. It is not yet clear if, or how, the 109th Congress might address this issue.

Rural Water Supply Projects

Beginning with authorization of the WEB Rural Water Supply Act in 1980 (P.L. 96-355), Congress has authorized the Bureau to fund the construction of several "rural water supply" projects and oversee construction of another, with funding coming from the Department of Agriculture. These projects have individual authorizations, but all are generally aimed at providing water for municipal and industrial (MandI) uses in rural areas — a departure from the historical mission of providing water for irrigation, with MandI use as an incidental project purpose. The most recent project to be approved is for Espanola New Mexico (P.L. 108-354). This legislation also includes authorization for a feasibility study for a Chimayo water supply system.

These projects have been somewhat controversial, largely due to the relatively large share of federal construction costs proposed. Typically, the Bureau requires that people benefitting from a reclamation project repay 100% of the construction costs (plus interest) attributed to MandI project purposes. For example, if a project's purpose is 50% irrigation, 30% flood control, and 20% MandI, MandI water users would pay (reimburse the federal government) for 100% of their 20% of construction costs of the project, plus interest (the federal cost share would be 0% of the 20% cost allocated to MandI purposes). In contrast, the federal cost share (non-reimbursable component) for the Bureau's "rural water supply" projects typically ranges from 75% to 85%. Some have raised concerns that these projects have the potential to overwhelm the Bureau's budget. For example, the federal contribution to the Lewis and Clark project is estimated at $214 million. For perspective, the Bureau's budget ranges in the neighborhood of approximately $800 million (net current authority) annually. Prior to the recent authorizations, the Bureau had approximately 60 authorized projects in various stages of construction with projected construction costs for completion of $4.9 billion. Outstanding construction authorizations now total approximately $7 billion (excluding "deferred" projects such as Auburn Dam).

Some also fear that these projects are outside the realm of those historically constructed by the Bureau and believe they would be better handled via other existing federal water quality or water supply programs, such as the USDA's Rural Utility Service or the EPA's state revolving loan fund. However, as designed, the projects do not fit EPA or USDA criteria, and thus project proponents have looked to the Bureau for funding. An additional concern with the Lewis and Clark legislation was that it authorized projects outside of the Bureau of Reclamation's historic service area (outside the 17 western states). (For information on other federal water supply programs, see CRS Report RL30478.)

In the 108th Congress, three bills were introduced addressing rural water supply issues. One bill would have authorized the Secretary of the Interior to establish a rural water supply program to plan, design, and construct projects in reclamation states as defined by the bill; a second would have assisted states and local communities in evaluating and developing rural and small community water supply systems; and a third would have authorized the BOR to coordinate and revamp its rural water supply activities. These bills differed according to factors such as the scope of their water supply program; eligibility criteria, program priorities, and implementation; ability to pay for construction, operation and maintenance; and feasibility studies and reporting requirements.

On May 11, 2005, the Senate Energy and Natural Resources Committee held a hearing on S. 895, a bill to establish a new rural water supply program to be administered by the Bureau of in Reclamation, Department of the Interior. The bill combines elements of three bills introduced in the 108th Congress: S. 1085 (Bingaman), S. 1732 (Domenici, by request), and S. 2218 (Domenici).

Title 16 Projects

Title 16 of P.L. 102-575 directs the Secretary of the Interior to develop a program to "investigate and identify" opportunities to reclaim and reuse wastewater and naturally impaired ground and surface water. The original act authorized construction of five reclamation wastewater projects and six wastewater and groundwater recycling/reclamation studies. The act was amended in 1996 (P.L. 104-206) to authorize another 18 construction projects and an additional study, and again in 1998 (P.L. 105-321) and 2000 (P.L. 106-554, Division B, Section 106) to authorize two more construction projects. Since then, several individual project authorizations amending the

Reclamation and Wastewater and Groundwater Study and Facilities Act have been passed, including three during the 108th Congress: P.L. 108-233, Irvine, CA; P.L. 108-7, North Las Vegas, NV (originally authorized in P.L. 104-206); and P.L. 108-361, Williamson County, Texas. Nine Title 16 bills (not including companion bills) have been introduced (see "Legislation," below) in the 109th Congress.

The general purpose of Title 16 projects is to provide supplemental water supplies by recycling/reusing agricultural drainage water, wastewater, brackish surface and groundwater, and other sources of contaminated water. Water reclaimed via Title 16 projects may be used for MandI water supply (non-potable purposes only), irrigation supply, groundwater recharge, fish and wildlife enhancement, or outdoor recreation. Projects may be permanent or for demonstration purposes. Project construction costs are shared by a local project sponsor or sponsors and the federal government. The federal share is generally limited to a maximum of 25% of total project costs and in most cases the federal share is non-reimbursable, resulting in a *de facto* grant to the local project sponsor(s). Congress limited the federal share of individual projects to $20 million beginning in 1996 (P.L. 104-266). The federal share of feasibility studies is limited to 50% of the total, except in cases of "financial hardship"; however, the federal share must be reimbursed. The Secretary may also accept in-kind services that are determined to positively contribute to the study.

The Bureau's water reclamation and wastewater recycling program is limited to projects and studies in the 17 western states authorized in the Reclamation Act of 1902, as amended (32 Stat. 388), unless specifically authorized by Congress.[1] Authorized recipients of program assistance include "legally organized non-federal entities" (e.g., irrigation districts, water districts, and municipalities). Construction funding is generally limited to projects where (1) an appraisal investigation and feasibility study have been completed and approved by the Secretary; (2) the Secretary has determined the project sponsor is capable of funding the nonfederal share of project costs; and (3) the local sponsor has entered a cost-share agreement committing to funding its share.

Total funding for the program for FY2003 was 30.6 million. The Title 16 program was also subject to the OMB program review, which ultimately led to a lower request of $12.6 million for FY2004. Total funding for Title 16 projects was $28.4 million for FY2004 and $23.0 million for FY2005. The Administration requested $10.2 million for FY2006.

Salton Sea

Federal and state agencies, and regional organizations, are currently working to determine the best alternative for restoring the Salton Sea. In P.L. 108-361, which reauthorized the CALFED Program, a provision was included stating that not later than December 2006, the Secretary of the Interior in coordination with the state of California and the Salton Sea Authority shall determine the best alternative for restoring the Salton Sea. Some restoration proposals have been suggested and alternatives for restoring the sea are tentatively expected to be selected by June 2005.

The Salton Sea is a large, inland water body in California that is saline-rich and is sustained by agricultural run-off from farmlands in nearby Imperial and Coachella valleys. It provides permanent and temporary habitat for many species of plants and animals, including several endangered species.[2] It also serves as an important recreational area for the region. The Salton Sea has been altered by increasing salinity caused by a steadily decreasing water table. High salinity levels have changed habitats and stressed several populations of plants and animals. The scope and costs of efforts to restore the Salton Sea was reported in a study done by the Department of the Interior in 2003.[3]

Several proposals have been floated to address Salton Sea issues. In July 2004, the Salton Sea Authority endorsed a restoration plan for the Salton Sea that calls for the construction of a causeway across the center of the sea. This would separate the sea into two basins, an 85,000-acre North Basin that would reach salinity levels similar to the ocean, and a southern section that would consist of wetlands areas as well as numerous recreational lakes ranging from freshwater to hyper-saline. The estimated cost of this project is between $650 and $730 million. This plan is now under review by the California Department of Water Resources. Funding for restoring the Salton Sea is expected to come from a restoration fund that will receive money from fees collected from water sales in the region. This fund was developed from a set of three bills enacted by the state of California on September 12, 2003, and is expected to generate up to $300 million for restoring the Salton Sea. As proposals for restoring the Salton Sea and related Colorado River issues continue to be negotiated during the 109th Congress, congressional oversight is expected to continue.

Legislation

Title 16 Projects

H.R. 122 (Issa)

To amend the Reclamation Wastewater and Groundwater Study and Facilities Act to authorize the Secretary of the Interior to participate in the Eastern Municipal Water District Recycled Water System Pressurization and Expansion Project. Introduced Jan. 4, 2005; referred to House Committee on Resources (Subcommittee on Water and Power).

H.R. 123 (Issa)

To amend the Reclamation Wastewater and Groundwater Study and Facilities Act to authorize the Secretary of the Interior to participate in the Elsinore Valley Municipal Water District Wildomar Service Area Recycled Water Distribution Facilities and Alberhill Wastewater Treatment and Reclamation Facility Projects. Introduced Jan. 4, 2005; referred to House Committee on Resources (Subcommittee on Water and Power).

H.R. 177 (Miller, Gary)

To amend the Reclamation Wastewater and Groundwater Study and Facilities Act to authorize the Secretary of the Interior to participate in the Prado Basin Natural Treatment System Project, to authorize the Secretary to carry out a program to assist agencies in projects to construct regional brine lines in California, to authorize the Secretary to participate in the Lower Chino Dairy Area desalination demonstration and reclamation project, and for other purposes. Introduced on Jan. 4, 2005; referred to House Committee on Resources (Subcommittee on Water and Power).

H.R. 497 (Sanchez)

To amend the Reclamation Wastewater and Groundwater Study and Facilities Act to increase the ceiling on the Federal share of the costs of phase I of the Orange County, California, Regional Water Reclamation Project. Introduced Feb. 1, 2005; referred to House Committee on Resources (Subcommittee on Water and Power).

H.R. 802 (Dreier)

To amend the Reclamation Wastewater and Groundwater Study and Facilities Act to authorize the Secretary of the Interior to participate in the

Inland Empire regional recycling project and in the Cucamonga Valley Water District recycling project. Introduced Feb. 15, 2005; referred to House Committee on Resources (Subcommittee on Water and Power). See also S. 746 (Feinstein).

H.R. 843 (Abercrombie), S. 264 (Akaka)

To amend the Reclamation Wastewater and Groundwater Study and Facilities Act to authorize certain projects in the State of Hawaii and to amend the Hawaii Water Resources Act of 2000; to modify the water resources study. Introduced Feb. 16, 2005; referred to House Committee on Resources (Subcommittee on Water and Power); reported favorably without amendment by the Senate Committee on Energy and Natural Resources (S.Rept. 109-33); placed on Senate Legislative Calendar under General Orders. Calendar No. 46 on March 10, 2005.

H.R. 855 (Ortiz)

To amend the Reclamation Wastewater and Groundwater Study and Facilities Act to authorize the Secretary of the Interior to participate in the Brownsville Public Utility Board water recycling and desalinization project. Introduced Feb. 16, 2005; referred to the House Committe on Resources (Subcommittee on Water and Power).

H.R. 863 (Reyes)

To amend the Reclamation Wastewater and Groundwater Study and Facilities Act to authorize the Secretary of the Interior to participate in the El Paso, Texas, water reclamation, reuse, and desalinization project, and for other purposes. Introduced Feb.16, 2005; referred to House Committee on Resources (Subcommittee on Water and Power).

S. 746 (Feinstein)

To amend the Reclamation Wastewater and Groundwater Study and Facilities Act to authorize the Secretary of the Interior to participate in the Inland Empire regional recycling project and in the Cucamonga Valley Water District recycling project. Introduced April 11, 2005; referred to Senate Committee on Energy and Natural Resources. See also H.R. 802 (Dreier).

Water Supply and Conservation

H.R. 125 (Issa)

To authorize the Secretary of the Interior to construct facilities to provide water for irrigation, municipal, domestic, military, and other uses from the Santa Margarita River, California, and for other purposes. Introduced Jan. 4, 2005; referred to House Committee on Resources (Subcommittee on Water and Power) and House Armed Services.

H.R. 135 (Linder)

To establish the "Twenty-First Century Water Commission" to study and develop recommendations for a comprehensive water strategy to address future water needs. Introduced Jan. 4, 2005; referred to House Committee on Resources (Subcommittee on Water and Power) and House Transportation and Infrastructure (Subcommittee on Water Resources and Environment); considered and passed under suspension of the rules on April 12, 2005; referred to Senate Committee on Environment and Public Works.

H.R. 386 (Hinojosa), S. 519 (Hutchinson)

To amend the Lower Rio Grande Valley Water Resources Conservation and Improvement Act of 2000 to authorize additional projects and activities under that act, and for other purposes. Introduced Jan. 26, 2005; referred to House Committee on Resources (Subcommittee on Water and Power); hearing held by Senate Committee on Energy and Natural Resources on April 19, 2005.

H.R. 524 (Berkley)

To amend the Internal Revenue Code of 1986 to provide incentives for the conservation of water. Introduced Feb. 2, 2005; referred to House Committee on Ways and Means.

H.R. 1008 (Calvert)

To authorize the Secretary of the Interior to participate in the design and construction of the Riverside-Corona Feeder in cooperation with the Western Municipal Water District of Riverside, California. Introduced March 1, 2005; referred to House Committee on Resources (Subcommittee on Water and Power).

H.R. 1046 (Cubin), S. 99 (Enzi)

To authorize the Secretary of the Interior to contract with the city of Cheyenne, Wyoming, for the storage of the city's water in the Kendrick Project, Wyoming. Introduced March 2, 2005; referred to the House Committee on Resources (Subcommittee on Water and Power); considered and passed under suspension of the rules on May 16, 2005; reported without amendment by Senate Committee on Energy and Natural Resources (S Rpt. 109-27) on March 10, 2005.

H.R. 1326 (Thompson)

To enable a Bureau of Reclamation partnership with the North Bay Water Reuse Authority and other regional partners to achieve water supply, water quality, and environmental restoration objectives. Introduced March 15, 2005; referred to House Committee on Resources.

S. 178 (Domenici), H.R. 1711 (Wilson)

A bill to provide assistance to the State of New Mexico for the development of comprehensive State water plans, and for other purposes. Introduced January 26, 2005. Mark-up session held Feb. 9, 2005; reported without amendment by Senate Committee on Energy and Natural Resources on March 7, 2005 (S.Rept. 109-16).

S. 247 (Smith, Gordon)

A bill to authorize the Secretary of the Interior to assist in the planning, design, and construction of the Tumalo Irrigation District Water Conservation Project in Deschutes County, Oregon. Introduced Feb. 1, 2005; referred to Senate Committee on Energy and Natural Resources.

S. 251 (Smith, Gordon)

A bill to authorize the Secretary of the Interior, acting through the Bureau of Reclamation, to conduct a water resource feasibility study for the Little Butte/Bear Creek Sub-basins in Oregon. Introduced Feb. 1, 2005 ; referred to Senate Committee on Energy and Natural Resources; hearings held April 19, 2005.

S. 353 (Conrad)

A bill to amend the Water Resources Development Act of 1999 to direct the Secretary of the Army to provide assistance to design and construct a project to provide a continued safe and reliable municipal water supply system for Devils Lake, North Dakota. Introduced Feb. 10, 2005; referred to Senate Committee on Environment and Public Works.

Miscellaneous

H.R. 487 (Pearce)

To impose limitations on the authority of the Secretary of the Interior to claim title or other rights to water absent specific direction of law or to abrogate, injure, or otherwise impair any right to the use of any quantity of water. Introduced Feb. 1, 2005; referred to the House Committee on Resources (Subcommittee on Water and Power).

S. 166 (Smith, Gordon)

A bill to amend the Oregon Resource Conservation Act of 1996 to reauthorize the participation of the Bureau of Reclamation in the Deschutes River Conservancy, and for other purposes. Introduced Jan. 25, 2005; referred to Senate Committee on Energy and Natural Resources; hearings held April 19, 2005.

S. 231 (Smith, Gordon)

A bill to authorize the Bureau of Reclamation to participate in the rehabilitation of the Wallowa Lake Dam in Oregon, and for other purposes. Introduced Feb. 1, 2005. Mark-up session held Feb. 9, 2005; reported without amendment by Senate Committee on Energy and Natural Resources on March 10, 2005 (S.Rept. 109-30).

S. 232 (Smith, Gordon)

A bill to authorize the Secretary of the Interior, acting through the Bureau of Reclamation, to assist in the implementation of fish passage and screening facilities at non-Federal water projects, and for other purposes. Introduced Feb. 1, 2005. Mark-up session held Feb. 9, 2005; reported without amendment by Senate Committee on Energy and Natural Resources on March 10, 2005 (S.Rept. 109-31).

S. 648 (Smith, Gordon)

To amend the Reclamation States Emergency Drought Relief Act of 1991 to extend the authority for drought assistance. Introduced March 17, 2005; referred to Senate Committee on Energy and Natural Resources.

S.728 (Bond)

To provide for the consideration and development of water and related resources, to authorize the Secretary of the Army to construct various projects for improvements to rivers and harbors of the United States, and for other purposes. Introduced April 6, 2005; referred to Senate Committee on Environment and Public Works; reported with amendments (S. Rpt.109-61); placed on Senate Legislative Calendar under General Orders. Calendar No. 93 on April 26, 2005.

S. 802 (Domenici)

To establish a National Drought Council within the Department of Agriculture, to improve national drought preparedness, mitigation, and response efforts, and for other purposes. Introduced April 14, 2005; referred to the Senate Committee on Agriculture, Nutrition, and Forestry.

S. 1017 (Chafee)

To reauthorize grants from the water resources research and technology institutes established under the Water Resources Research Act of 1984. Introduced May 12, 2005; referred to Senate Committee on Environment and Public Works.

REFERENCES

[1] Section 103(a)(4) of P.L. 106-566 directs the Secretary of the Interior to study recycling, reclamation, and reuse of water and wastewater for agricultural and non-agricultural uses in the state of Hawaii.

[2] The Salton Sea is considered an important stopover for birds on the Pacific flyway.

[3] U.S. Department of the Interior, Bureau of Reclamation, *Salton Sea Study: Status Report*, January 2003.

In: Planning and Managing of Water Resources ISBN 1-59454-757-2
Editor: Peter A. Unwal, pp. 23-48

Chapter 2

UPPER MISSISSIPPI RIVER SYSTEM: PROPOSALS TO RESTORE AN INLAND WATERWAY'S ECOSYSTEM*

Kyna Powers and Nicole T. Carter

SUMMARY

Recent proposals to expand the Upper Mississippi River-Illinois Waterway (UMR-IWW) — a major transportation route for products moving to and from Illinois, Iowa, Minnesota, Missouri, and Wisconsin — have met with significant controversy. Some of this controversy centers on the cumulative environmental effects of the current navigation system and the proposed expansion. The Upper Mississippi River System (UMRS) — which includes the navigation channel and surrounding floodplain — supports an unusually large number of species for a temperate river. The UMR-IWW navigation system alters UMRS habitat and contributes to a decline in the abundance of some species. For example, locks, dams, and other channel structures inhibit the movement of fish between and within river segments; fill side channels, backwaters, and wetlands with sediment; and suppress plant growth by reducing water clarity.

---

* Excerpted from CRS Report RL32630, dated June 23, 2005.

In 2001, in response to criticism that draft navigation feasibility studies did not look at navigation's cumulative environmental effects, the Corps restructured its feasibility study to include an ecosystem restoration component. In late September 2004, the Corps released a final feasibility report recommending that Congress approve a 50-year framework for combined ecosystem restoration and navigation improvements. The ecosystem restoration component is aimed at maintaining and restoring a broad array of habitats and ecosystem processes at a total cost of $5.3 billion for the 50-year plan. Authorization of an initial set of both restoration projects at $1.58 billion and navigation projects at $2.03 billion has been proposed in the 109th Congress. (For a discussion of proposed legislation, see CRS Report RL32915, *Upper Mississippi River-Illinois Waterway Investments: Legislation in the 109th Congress*, by Nicole T. Carter and Kyna Powers.)

The federal responsibility (and more specifically the role of the Corps) for restoring ecosystems altered by federal projects is still being defined. Consequently, the scope of large-scale restoration efforts and the federal/non-federal cost-share are being developed largely on a case-by-case basis. The Corps' UMRS restoration plan recommends actions limited to the navigation system and its floodplain, with federal responsibility for more than 90% of the cost. The underlying question is whether, or in what form, Congress will authorize and appropriate funds for ecosystem restoration on the UMRS. If authorized, UMRS restoration would be the Corps' second large-scale restoration effort and the first large-scale restoration effort for a high-volume commercial waterway.

This chapter explains what is meant by restoration and why the UMRS ecosystem is being considered for restoration, the Corps' restoration plan, and some of the issues in the debate over federal investment in this restoration.

CONGRESSIONAL AUTHORIZATION CONTEXT

Navigation-Ecosystem Restoration Authorization Decision

Federal efforts to restore ecosystems over wide areas are being planned and initiated around the country. Restoration of the Upper Mississippi River System (UMRS) — the navigable portions of the Upper Mississippi River, Illinois Waterway, and other tributaries, and the associated floodplain (see

Figure 1)[1] — is one of these efforts. Congress must authorize restoration investments before implementation can begin. The U.S. Army Corps of Engineers (Corps) has developed a plan for UMRS restoration as part of an effort to study measures to improve navigation efficiency on the Upper Mississippi River-Illinois Waterway (UMR-IWW) navigation system —a major transportation route for goods into and out of Illinois, Iowa, Minnesota, Missouri, and Wisconsin. The UMR-IWW includes 1,200 miles of navigable waterways and many navigational improvements (see Figure 2). According to commercial users of the navigation system — primarily shippers and agricultural producers — it has been beset by increasing traffic congestion and delays related to aging infrastructure and limitations of existing lock capacity.

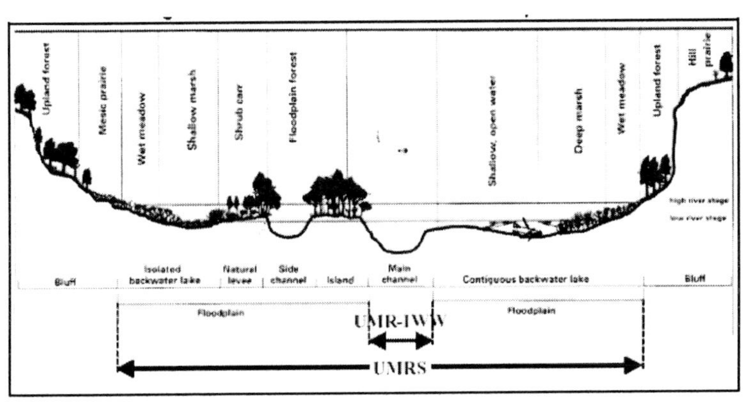

Source: Corps, Final Integrated Feasibility Report and PEIS, p. 4.

Figure 1. UMRS and UMR-IWW Comparison

To inform the congressional decision on whether to authorize investments in navigation and ecosystem restoration, the Corps released a *Final Integrated Feasibility Report and Programmatic Environmental Impact Statement for the UMR-IWW System Navigation Feasibility Study* in late September 2004.[2] The report proposes a 50-year plan for combined UMR-IWW navigation and UMRS restoration investments and recommends expanding the project purpose of the UMR-IWW to include ecosystem restoration, thus facilitating dual-purpose management. From the 50-year plan, the Corps recommends authorization of a first increment of investments — $1.88 billion for seven new locks and small-scale navigation measures, and $1.46 billion for a 15-year ecosystem restoration effort. A recommendation by the Corps' Chief of Engineers was released December

15, 2004 and sent to the Assistant Secretary of the Army (Civil Works) for further review. From there it will undergo review by the Office of Management and Budget (OMB).

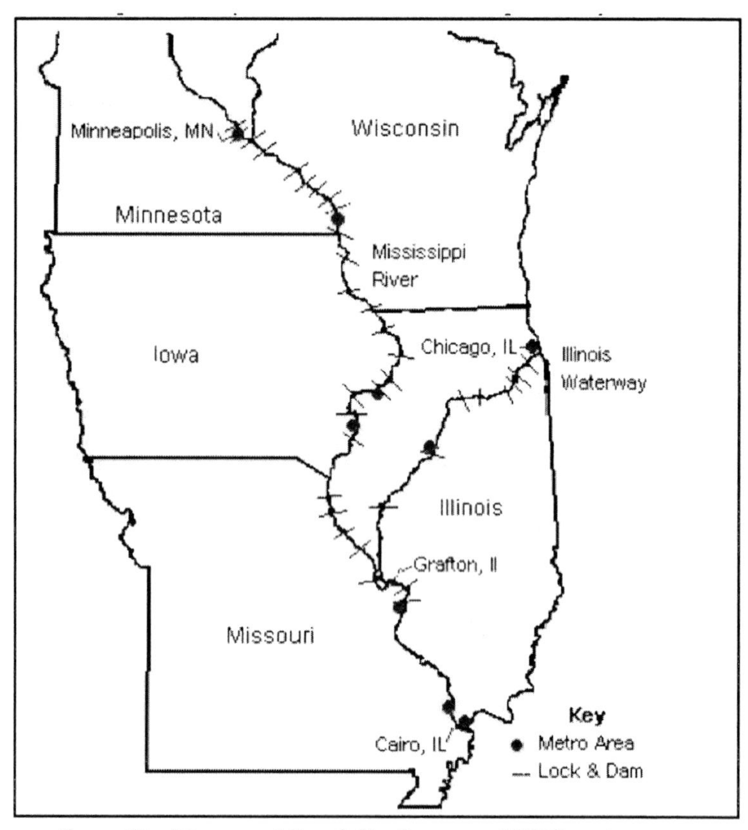

Source: Corps, Final Integrated Feasibility Report and PEIS, p. 4.

Figure 2. Map of the UMR-IWW Navigation System

This report describes the context for the congressional decision to authorize ecosystem restoration investments.[3] First, the report provides a brief introduction and explains the ecosystem change of the UMRS. Second, it reviews the Corps' preferred and alternative plans, including the Corps' preferred 50-year plan, alternative 50-year plans, and the first 15-year increment. Last, this report presents key aspects of the debate over the congressional authorization of an ecosystem restoration effort, including the magnitude and cost, cost-share, scope, and linkage between ecosystem restoration and navigation investments. (For information on the navigation decision, see CRS Issue Brief IB10133, *Water Resources Development Act: Army Corps of Engineers Authorization Issues in the 109th Congress,* coordinated by Nicole T. Carter.)

Evolution of Ecosystem Restoration Plan

The Corps' feasibility study, which began in 1993 to investigate the long-run navigation needs of the UMR-IWW, has been the subject of much controversy. In particular, allegations contending that the Corps manipulated a benefit-cost analysis to support UMR-IWW navigation lock expansion and the subsequent investigation are cited by some Corps observers as evidence that fundamental changes need to be made in the Corps project development and approval process.[4] The Corps had also been criticized by state and federal natural resource agencies and environmental groups, since the early years of the study, for not including mitigation of environmental impacts beyond the incremental environment impacts of lock expansion; the National Research Council (NRC) of the National Academy of Sciences repeated this criticism in a 2001 report reviewing the feasibility study.[5] In response in 2001, the Corps reformulated the economic analysis and added an ecosystem restoration component to the study to examine measures to address the cumulative environmental impacts of navigation and other stressors of the UMRS ecosystem. The NRC continues to review the study. A second NRC panel produced a report in December 2003 that reviews the reformulated study,[6] and another report in October 2004 that comments on a draft Corps feasibility report from April 2004.[7] The same NRC panel is working on another report.

The Corps' reformulated analysis has not significantly reduced the debate over the urgency, necessity, and national benefit of expanded navigation capacity. The Corps' ecosystem restoration plan has been less controversial, with the discussion being largely focused on the magnitude and cost of the restoration effort, the federal/non-federal cost-share, the scope of the restoration effort (i.e., a focus on the navigation project or the larger watershed), and the linkage between navigation and restoration for river management and federal investments.

Legislation

Although the Assistant Secretary of the Army (Civil Works) and the OMB have not completed their reviews, the 109th Congress has introduced two bills to authorize ecosystem restoration as part UMR-IWW investments. These bills — S. 728 and H.R. 2864 (Water Resources Development Act (WRDA)of 2004) —would authorize many of the investments the Corps recommended; each would authorize $2.03 billion for navigation, and $1.58 billion for ecosystem restoration. These bills are discussed further in CRS Report RL32915, *Upper Mississippi River-Illinois Waterway Investments: Legislation in the 109th Congress,* by Nicole T. Carter and Kyna Powers.

UMRS Ecosystem Change

Congress identified the UMRS as a nationally significant ecosystem and commercial navigation system in the Water Resources Development Act (WRDA) of 1986 (P.L. 99-662). According to the Corps and basin state representatives, the UMRS ecosystem is in decline and action is needed if further degradation is to be avoided.[8] The UMRS has been changed by multiple factors, with the construction of navigation infrastructure and water management for navigation being principal among these factors. Thirty-seven lock and dams and channel training structures that create a 9-foot deep navigation channel alter the distribution and movement of river water. These changes allow for low-cost transportation between the Upper Mississippi River Basin and the Gulf of Mexico's ocean ports; however, these structures also inhibit the movement of some animal species between and within river segments; fill side channels, backwaters, and wetlands with sediment; and suppress plant growth by reducing water clarity. Other factors also have contributed to ecosystem decline, including land-use practices in the watershed that cause sediment to enter the system and levees that isolate floodplains from the river. The Mississippi and Illinois Rivers also have a long history of impaired water quality attributable to contamination from agricultural, industrial, residential, and municipal sources. Figure 3 shows the Upper Mississippi-Illinois River watershed — the area drained by the two rivers and their tributaries. The watershed, at 121 million acres (190,000 square miles; 6% of the lower 48 states), is much larger than the UMRS, which is limited to the navigable river reaches and associated floodplains and covers 2.5 million acres (3,900 square miles).

UMRS Significance

According to the U.S. Geological Survey (USGS), the UMRS is one of the nation's greatest ecological "treasures."[9] Due to the complexity of the system and its north-south orientation, the UMRS is unique among large temperate rivers in that it supports an unusually large number of fish species.[10] More than 150 species of freshwater fish (25% of all North American fish) have been reported to inhabit the UMRS. Overall, the UMRS provides temporary or permanent habitat to more than 485 species of fish, birds, and animals.[11] The UMRS also supports recreational opportunities. Annually, there are 12 million recreational visits to the UMRS;[12] boating, sightseeing, sports fishing, hunting, and trapping are some of the more popular recreational uses.[13] It is estimated that recreation activities generate $1.2 billion and over 18,000 jobs annually.[14]

Congress has recognized the importance of UMRS habitat since early in the 20th century. Congress established the Upper Mississippi River National Wildlife and Fish Refuge in 1924, but specified that it is not to interfere with navigation.[15] It provides 242,400 acres of habitat for migratory and local birds, animals, wildflowers and aquatic plants, fish, and other aquatic life. This refuge, which is administered by the U.S. Fish and Wildlife Service, covers 261 miles along the Mississippi River.

Ecosystem Decline

Although the UMRS provides recreation and species habitat, the federal infrastructure on the UMR-IWW was authorized by Congress for the purpose of navigation. The Corps manages the Upper Mississippi River and the Illinois River to provide a 9-foot navigation channel. To create this channel, the rivers were transformed from free-flowing rivers into a series of separated navigation pools behind locks and dams. These changes in the hydrologic regime alter water quality parameters, such as temperature, dissolved oxygen, and sediment transport, thereby ultimately affecting fish and wildlife and terrestrial and aquatic ecosystem processes, such as intermittent inundation and drying.[16]

Consequently, side channels, backwater, and wetlands are filling in with sediment (see Figure 1). While the loss of total aquatic habitat (1.4%)[17] may be small, the proportional loss of backwaters exceeded 10% in more than half of the reaches examined.[18] Some of the reaches are projected to lose from 20 to 30 percent of their backwaters in the next 50 years."[19]

Under current sedimentation rates, many backwater areas throughout the UMRS will probably become terrestrial areas within the next 50 to 100 years.[20] Including fish, mammals, birds, and amphibians, the UMRS is home to 36 federally listed rare, threatened, or endangered species.

Source: Upper Mississippi River Basin Association, at [http://www.umrba.org/basinfacts.htm]

Figure 3. Upper Mississippi and Illinois River Watershed

According to the United States Geological Survey, mussels are a good indicator of ecosystem health. While 50 species of mussels were once found in the UMRS, recent surveys have documented a drop to 30 species, two of which are federally listed as endangered.[21] This decrease may indicate a broader ecosystem decline.

Ecosystem changes have not reduced the number of fish species found in the UMRS. However, they have affected the distribution and abundance of some species.[22] For example, lack of suitable winter habitat threatens some popular backwater species, including bluegill, crappies, and large mouth bass.[23] The river also contains a federally listed endangered fish — the pallid sturgeon — and over 50 state-listed rare, threatened, or endangered fish.[24]

Responding to Decline

In response to ecosystem changes, environmental enhancement projects have been undertaken since WRDA 1986 in which Congress established the Environmental Management Program for the UMRS. The EMP consists of habitat rehabilitation/enhancement projects and a long-term resource monitoring program. Under the EMP, the Corps has completed more than 40 habitat rehabilitation and enhancement projects, improving habitat on almost 67,000 acres.[25] Another eight projects are under construction, and 16 are in the design stages. Together, these additional projects will improve approximately 74,000 acres of riverine and floodplain habitat.[26] According to the Corps, current annual environmental investments — $33.9 million, on average, in federal and state funds — are inadequate to prevent continued degradation.[27]

Pointing to indicators of ecosystem decline, many groups are concerned about the long-term effects of continued ecosystem alteration and argue for further investments in ecosystem restoration that will support habitat diversity. Some cite the loss of migratory birds in the areas of the Illinois River and the Middle and Lower Mississippi River as examples of a possible outcome if investments are not made.[28] Environmental groups want to reverse ecosystem decline and to increase the services and benefits provided by a healthy ecosystem (e.g., recreational uses).

THE CORPS' PROPOSAL FOR ECOSYSTEM RESTORATION

Corps' Preferred Ecosystem Restoration Plan

The Corps proposes in its *Final Feasibility Report and PEIS* to reverse ecosystem decline by making investments in restoration at the same time as investing in navigation expansion. The report puts forth a preferred alternative for a dual-purpose UMR-IWW navigation and UMRS ecosystem restoration plan — $2.4 billion in navigation improvements and $5.3 billion for ecosystem restoration over 50 years.[29] Under the Corps' recommended cost-share option, $4.25 billion in measures under the ecosystem restoration plan, more than 80% of the total, would be paid for 100% by the federal government as they would address impacts from the existing 9-foot navigation project or for activities on federal lands. The remaining $1.05 billion would be for floodplain restoration, backwater water level management, backwater dredging/restoration, island and shoreline protection, measures to increase topographic diversity of the floodplain, and some adaptive management activities; the costs would be shared with local sponsors (65% federal and 35% non-federal; $680 million federal and $370 million non-federal).

Unlike most of the Corps' mitigation efforts for its other projects, the Corps' preferred UMRS restoration plan is not focused on particular species. Instead it is aimed at restoring an array of aquatic and terrestrial species; because of this more systemic approach, the preferred restoration plan combines multiple categories of measures that together are expected to benefit the physical, chemical, and biological health of the entire UMRS ecosystem. The Corps' preferred ecosystem restoration plan contains a total of 1,009 measures, including 248 for island building and protection, 14 for fish passage, 40 for floodplain restoration, 21 for water level management and dam operations, 208 for backwater restoration, 147 for side channel restoration, 64 for wing dam/dike alternation, 235 for shoreline protection, and 32 for topographic diversity. Because habitat is seen as a key component in restoring species diversity and abundance,[30] habitat is used as a gauge of what will be achieved under each measure; the 1,009 measures are estimated to influence a total of 703,717 acres of habitat — many times the level of effort under the existing EMP.

According to the Corps, the needed environmental and social mitigation for harm caused by the ecosystem restoration measures would be minimal.

The *Final Feasibility Report and PEIS* indicates that the selected restoration alternative would have a net positive effect on ecosystem goods and services and no effect on commercial navigation, water supply, or hydroelectric power. It stated that navigation pool drawdowns could harm livestock watering and recreational boating, but the effects would be minimal. Moreover, recreational boating may see an overall benefit from restoration investments.

Integrated Navigation and Ecosystem Management

The Corps' feasibility report recommends that the restoration measures be implemented within the context of a new overall dual-purpose management framework. Today, navigation is the sole purpose of the Corps UMR-IWW project, and ecosystem restoration activities are conducted separately under the EMP. The Corps recommends creating a structure for UMR-IWW/UMRS investments and operations consisting of three basic elements:

- adding ecosystem restoration as a UMR-IWW project purpose, creating a dual-purpose navigation and restoration authority,[31]
- approving a combined navigation and ecosystem restoration plan as a framework,[32] and
- adaptively implementing navigation investments and adaptively managing ecosystem restoration investments.[33]

According to the Corps, these three elements combined would allow the agency to proceed with operational changes and near-term investments for navigation and ecosystem restoration. Investments would be planned as part of a long-term combined river management framework that minimizes risk by establishing a process to incorporate acquired information into ongoing decision-making, known as adaptive management, and they would be authorized in phases. According to the Corps, integrated management of the environmental and navigation purposes will improve operational efficiency, resulting in cost-savings and synergistic benefits.[34] The Corps also argues that dual-purpose authorization would give it flexibility to use operation and maintenance funds for ecosystem restoration and for navigation.[35]

A representative of the Upper Mississippi River Basin Association testified before Congress that the "states enthusiastically supported the Corps' decision to restructure the study, consistent with [their] long-standing commitment to integrated management of the river."[36] A number of agencies and non-governmental organizations also support dual-purpose authorization. A barge industry group also testified that it supports the ecosystem restoration plan, but believes that ecosystem restoration should be implemented without adversely affecting the growth of navigation.[37] Moreover, entities such as the National Corn Growers Association and the Midwest Area River Coalition 2000, do not support dual-purpose operation or integration of operation and maintenance for navigation and ecosystem restoration, citing that an existing backlog of navigation operation and maintenance (OandM) activities and a lack of clarity regarding implementation criteria for integrating operations.[38]

Adaptive Management

The third component of the Corps' proposed management framework is adaptive management. Adaptive management is a mechanism for dealing with the uncertainty of undertaking a large-scale, multi-year effort to change a complex system. The adaptive management component of the Corps' plan, which is budgeted for $653 million, calls for a scientific panel, system level learning, and restoration plan bio-response monitoring.[39] This approach is a recognition that identifying and eliminating all uncertainties involved with restoration before initiating a project is impossible. Furthermore, reducing uncertainties consumes time and money, and may delay the initiation of restoration efforts, thus leading to further ecosystem degradation.

While the built-in flexibility of adaptive management is seen as an asset for coping with uncertainty, adaptive management can be seen as risky because there is the potential that it could be used to justify delays in implementing important activities or to abandon previously set goals. Moreover, adaptive management is a relatively recent management approach, thus contributing its own uncertainties. Entities, such as the National Corn Growers Association has expressed concerns about adaptive management, but hopes that the Corps will continue to work closely with stakeholders. However, the U.S. Environmental Protection Agency, the basin states and environmental organizations support the Corps' proposal for adaptive management for UMRS restoration.

The October 2004 NRC report found the adaptive approach to be vital to the integrity of the Corps' preferred plan for combined ecosystem restoration and navigation investments. It states that the preferred plan:

> ... provides for a program of incremental implementation, an excellent framework for comprehensive adaptive management. If the Corps is provided the resources — and if it commits to the needed data collection, improved modeling techniques, and evaluation — many of

> the flaws and omissions in this study can be corrected in the course of implementation by the application of adaptive management principles.[40]

At the same time, the NRC was critical of the Corps for not defining "a clear, science-based framework for implementation, monitoring, and evaluation."[41]

Preferred and Alternative Plans

In addition to describing the Corps' preferred restoration plan and an integrated management framework, the feasibility report also describes how the Corps arrived at its recommendation. In selecting its preferred plan, the Corps analyzed five 50-year options for ecosystem restoration.[42] Each of these alternatives has a different target, and, therefore, requires a different level of investment. The Corps describes alternatives (A-E) by scope as follows:[43]

(A) **Without Project Condition** — No action, current environmental management activities continue;
(B) **No Net Loss** — Protect and maintain existing environmental diversity;
(C) **First Increment of Restoration** — Restore the habitats most directly affected by the navigation project;
(D) **Restoration to an Intermediate Level** — Restore broad array of habitat types using management practices and cost effective actions; and
(E) **Restoration to a High Level** — Restore to include most environmental objectives that can be accomplished in the context of the navigation project.

As shown in Table 1, the number of measures to be undertaken under the alternatives varies from no additional actions above the current EMP investments (Alternative A) to 1,202 measures (Alternative E). Within some categories of measures, the differentiation between alternatives is pronounced. The most dramatic difference is the number of fish passage projects and floodplain restoration plans (see Table 1). While there would be no fish passage at dam sites under Alternatives A through C, Alternative D has 14 and Alternative E has 33. For floodplain restoration specifically,

Alternatives B and C have 2 and 5 projects, respectively, while Alternative D has 40 projects and Alternative E has 80 projects.[44]

The level of investment under each restoration plan also affects the plans' expected benefits — measured by the Corps in *acres of influence[45]* — and cost. With the exception of the no-action alternative, the number of acres influenced by the projects increase from 148 thousand acres under Alternative B to 1,227 thousand acres under Alternative E. Similarly, the associated costs increase from $1.7 to $8.4 billion as the number of projects increase from Alternative B to Alternative E (see Table 1).

Table 1. Corps Analyzed Ecosystem Restoration Alternatives

	Restoration Alternatives				
	A	B	C	D	E
Total No. of Ecosystem Measures	0	617	808	1,010[a]	1,202
Fish Passage Measures	0	0	0	14	33
Floodplain Restoration Measures	0	2	5	40	80
Total Acres of Influence (in thousands)	0	148	252	704	1,227
Construction and Other First Costs (millions)	$0	$1,692	$2,817	$5,300[a]	$8,417

Source: Corps, *Final Feasibility Report and PEIS.* [a] These estimates include embankment lowering to promote connectivity and measures to decrease water level fluctuations on the IWW. These are refinements to the D plan made by the Corps, that is referred to in the final report as D*.

Plan Selection

The Corps evaluated its five ecosystem restoration alternatives using a combination of qualitative analyses and estimated quantitative outputs. Qualitative assessments included ecosystem diversity, ability to address ecosystem objectives, maintenance and enhancement of ecosystem goods and services, acceptability, and adaptability.[46] Quantitative measures included costs, acres of influence, cost effectiveness, ecosystem completeness, and regional economic development. From this evaluation, the Corps rated Alternatives D and E as close in their overall ranking, but recommended Alternative D. Specifically, "Alternative D was identified as the preferred alternative primarily because it is likely to achieve a high degree of completeness and diversity in the most efficient manner."[47] While the basin states and environmental organizations generally support the Corps preferred alternative (D*), a number of entities, including the U.S.

EPA, the U.S. Fish and Wildlife Service, and a number of basin states would prefer the more extensive alternative E.

In its analysis, the Corps compared environmental benefits with the cost of achieving those benefits. This comparison is called a cost effectiveness analysis. A cost effectiveness analysis is used as an optimization technique to identify either the least costly alternative for an established policy objective that defines the level of benefits desired or to maximize what can be achieved for a given investment. In the case of the *Final Feasibility Report and PEIS*, the Corps does not use cost effectiveness analysis for either of these purposes. Instead, the alternatives analyzed describe a range of benefits for a range of investments. That is, each of the five analyzed alternatives generates a different quantity of benefits, measured as acres of influence. Benefits were estimated by examining the acres of habitat affected through restoration activities under the EMP. Comparing acres of influence and cost helps the Corps to compare alternative plans; however, the usefulness of the comparison is limited by the fact that different acres of habitat are of different quality. Moreover, the Corps analysis is not particularly useful for comparing the benefits and costs of the UMRS restoration effort with the benefits and costs of other large-scale restoration efforts or Corps flood control and navigation investments.[48]

The Corps' Proposal for a 15-Year First Increment

After analyzing the 50-year alternatives, the Corps recommends approval of a 50-year framework for ecosystem restoration investments, and authorization of a first 15-year increment at $1.46 billion.[49] Following the Corps' preferred cost-sharing option, most projects would be a 100% federal responsibility, and some would be cost-shared with non-federal sponsors. Overall, responsibility for construction costs and other first costs (e.g., land acquisition) would be approximately 91% federal ($1.33 billion) and 9% non-federal ($0.13).[50] In addition to the first-cost, the Corps estimates that operating and maintaining the ecosystem restoration components will cost $76 million.[51] The Corps would likely be responsible for operation and maintenance (OandM) costs associated with fish passage facilities, water level management, and dike and wing dam alterations. These costs are estimated at $12 million. The remaining $64 million would be borne primarily by the U.S. Fish and Wildlife Service and the states. The cost share allocation is currently unclear. However, OandM costs associated with floodplain restoration projects would largely be paid by the states and nonprofit entities and the U.S. Fish and Wildlife Service would likely assume responsibility for operating and maintaining completed habitat projects.[52]

While the feasibility report does not include an analysis of alternative 15-year increments, the Corps states that measures were selected to provide (1) the best return on investment, (2) the best gains in habitat and species diversity, and (3) additional knowledge that will facilitate adaptive implementation of the 50-year plan. The Corps also selected measures for which there would be sufficient time to plan, design, construct, and monitor within the 15-year time frame.[53] However, some environmental organizations contend that a 15-year time frame is insufficient to achieve tangible results and that a longer-term authorization is needed. The U.S. Fish and Wildlife Service, for example, states that there will be a need for ecosystem restoration authority for as long as the navigation system is operated and maintained.[54] On the other hand, the state of Wisconsin supports the 15-year time frame on the basis that it will likely allow time to document the need for Alternative E. As it stands, the Corps' proposed 15-year increment includes 225 measures, under three main activities:[55]

- *Fish Passage and Dam Operations.* Fish migration is largely impeded by the locks and dams on the navigation system. To help fish stocks move more freely through the system, the 15-year plan would include about 30% of the fish passage and dam operations measures recommended in the 50-year plan. Specifically, the 15-year plan would include fish passage construction at 4 dams and fish passage planning and design at 2 dams ($209 million), and new dam operating procedures (and related land acquisition or easements) at 2 dams ($41 million). (**$250 million total — 100% federal**).
- *Programmatic Restoration Authority.* Programmatic authority to improve a wide array of habitat types through island building, floodplain restoration, water level management, backwater restoration, side channel restoration, wing dam/dike alternation and shoreline protection. (**$935 million total, not to exceed $25 million/measure — 100% federal**).
- *Land Acquisition.* The 50-year plan includes the acquisition of approximately 105,000 acres of floodplain and other riparian habitat. The 15-year plan would work to restore about 40% of that acreage. Specifically, it would include land acquisition of 35,000 acres from willing sellers, for floodplain connectivity and wetland

and riparian habitat protection and restoration. (**$277 million total — 65% federal**).

DEBATE OVER THE CORPS' ECOSYSTEM RESTORATION PROPOSAL

If Congress decides to authorize an ecosystem restoration plan for the UMRS, it will face a number of policy decisions. The more contentious aspects of such authorization may deal with the plan's magnitude and cost, cost-share, scope, and relationship to authorization of navigation investments and navigation operations. These decisions are briefly described below.

Restoration Magnitude and Cost

The Corps' analysis of ecosystem restoration includes five alternative plans of which restoration goals can be achieved at different levels of investment. Policymakers are now confronted with deciding on the magnitude of restoration efforts, if any, to be undertaken. Should the restoration effort *maintain* existing ecosystem conditions (i.e., no net loss), or should it *restore* ecosystem conditions without trying to attain some pre-existing situation? If restoration is the objective, how much of the earlier ecosystem function should be restored? Answers to these questions are based on value judgements and depend on balancing what the federal government and the basin states are willing to invest in restoration with the desire for a restored ecosystem.

As previously described, the Corps' $5.3 billion restoration plan would maintain and restore ecosystem function. One factor that some restoration supporters argue should be considered in deciding on federal investments is the relative spending on restoration and navigation. Implementing the Corps' 50-year restoration plan would result in an average annual cost (including both initial investments and OandM) of almost $140 million; this compares to the $185 million, on average, annually spent on the OandM and rehabilitation of the existing navigation system, and the additional $60 million annually for implementing the Corps' 50-year navigation plan.[56]

Cost-Share

Another investment consideration is the distribution of financial responsibility among federal and non-federal sponsors. The UMRS restoration plan raises the question of who is responsible for paying for restoration of ecosystems partially damaged by existing federal projects. Since WRDA 1986, non-federal sponsors have been responsible for a greater portion of Corps project costs; the cost-share formulas evolved out of a debate over having beneficiaries (i.e., non-federal sponsors) pay for the benefits received by footing a portion of project costs.[57] The established cost-share for Corps' ecosystem restoration projects is 65% federal / 35% non-federal; however, the Corps recommends for the UMRS a cost-share arrangement that increases federal responsibility because of the role of the federal UMR-IWW navigation system in earlier degradation, the extensive federal land holdings, and the multi-state nature of the effort. The recommended arrangement, which is generally supported by the states, agencies, and environmental and navigation organizations, would result in the $5.3 billion of restoration costs being split 91% federal / 9% non-federal. This cost share could be viewed as reflecting federal responsibility for mitigating damage caused by existing federal projects. Other federal agencies, basin states, environmental organizations, and the NRC support the Corps' proposed cost-share; observers outside the basin and others less likely to be direct beneficiaries of investments may argue that non-federal beneficiaries should pay a higher portion of the cost.

Although the Corps provides a justification for the dominance of federal financing, some observers may dispute this dominance for various reasons. One reason stems from part of the perceived motivation for adopting cost-share arrangements in WRDA 1986: "The cost-share formulas can't guarantee that every new project will be worth the price. But they will force state and local interests to weigh the costs against the benefits more conscientiously."[58] In this view, one purpose of cost-sharing is to put Corps projects to a "market test," whereby state and local beneficiaries confirm the value of a project by agreeing to share in the cost;[59] another benefit is that nonfederal sponsors may have a greater sense of project ownership. In contrast, the absence of local financial involvement can be seen as particularly problematic for a restoration project which lacks a benefit-cost analysis that identifies the level of investments at which the costs outweigh the benefits of longer term ecosystem services supporting human/economic endeavors and other societal values. On the other hand, one could argue that the willingness of a local partner to pay for ecosystem restoration does not provide an accurate litmus test given the ecosystem's national significance. Some environmental organizations are concerned with how the costs-share arrangement will effect the Corps' restoration priorities; they fear that requiring the non-federal sponsors to contribute 35% for some activities will discourage the Corps from aggressively pursuing these activities, particularly floodplain management activities.

A second objection to the dominance of federal financing for UMRS restoration may be that the available federal funding for UMRS restoration could be a constraint on restoration progress. The federal government, and the Corps in particular, is or may become involved in other large-scale, multi-billion dollar restoration efforts, such as the Florida Everglades restoration and the Coastal Louisiana wetlands restoration. This growing financial commitment to restoration investments is happening within the context of large projected federal budget deficits and a backlog of Corps construction projects currently estimated at more than $40 billion.

Restoration Scope

The Corps constrained the restoration plan by limiting its geographic scope. The Corps' plan targets restoration for the UMRS, that is, the UMR-IWW and its floodplain. As a result, reducing stressors that are beyond the floodplain in the larger watershed are not included among the recommended measures; instead the plan recommends measures to address the symptoms of these stressors. That is, the Corps' restoration plan does not include changes to land use practices related to increased sedimentation and degradation of other water quality parameters, flood damage reduction practices on a large-scale, or significant alterations to navigation infrastructure. For example, the Corps' plan recommends backwater dredging measures; dredging addresses the symptom of elevated sedimentation, but not the land use practices that can cause it, because these practices are considered outside the scope of the navigation study and navigation project. Substantial restoration benefits are not in the Corps' plan because they would interfere with navigation.

The Corps also limits the recommended restoration measures to the scope of the navigation project and study; that is, the measures are to address the cumulative impacts of operations of federal projects and other ecosystem stressors, without harming navigation. For example, dramatic water level changes that could produce substantial restoration benefits are not in the Corps' plan because they would interfere with navigation.

The NRC recommended in its December 2003 report that the Corps should, to the extent feasible, use a more holistic approach that includes factors such as water quality, flood damage reduction, and sediment transport. The Corps maintains that a more comprehensive, watershed-type approach is beyond the scope of the authorization under which the agency is conducting the feasibility study.[60] According to the Corps, another reason for the current restoration scope is that the five basin states support the concept that the study should remain focused on navigation and an environmentally sustainable navigation system.[61] Because only some of the stressors causing ecosystem degradation are managed under the Corps plan, not all of the ecosystem's natural river processes are restored, resulting in the need for regular human intervention to obtain some restoration benefits. Some environmental organizations, such as American Rivers, would prefer to have ecosystem restoration authorized for the entire watershed; activities under the Corps proposal would be limited in scope to the UMRS. The October 2004 NRC report showed less concern about the geographic scope of the restoration effort, and was more interested in restoring natural river processes that shape floodplains.[62] Consequently, the NRC supports not only dual purpose authorization, but also multi-purpose authorization that includes flood management.[63] Would a more comprehensive watershed approach accomplish restoration at less cost in the long-run, and if so, would this reduced cost be offset by potential constraints on navigation and flood damage reduction benefits?

Linked Authorization

As described above, the Corps limited the scope of its ecosystem restoration proposal to the navigation channel and surrounding floodplain. The Corps selected this scope because restoration plans were developed in the context of the navigation study; that is, the study has restoration as half of a dual-purpose plan. The environmental community uniformly support the need for restoration investments and dual-purpose management. The community, however, is not united on how to achieve this. Some environmental groups,[64] such as the Mississippi River Basin Alliance and Audubon, support authorizing a package of restoration and navigation investments within a dual purpose management context. Other environmental groups would like to see additional ecosystem restoration authorized through the existing structure of the EMP, without authorizing large-scale investments in navigation.

Legislation on the Corps proposal could link navigation funding to ecosystem restoration. Alternatively, legislation could authorize ecosystem restoration without authorizing the navigation project, or vice versa.[65] Should authorization or funding for ecosystem restoration and navigation be linked? If so, how closely should they be joined? These questions apply beyond the Corps' proposal for the UMR-IWW/UMRS to other Corps projects and other federal restoration efforts. As the first combined large-scale navigation and ecosystem restoration project, it could set a precedent for future proposals. What is the threshold for adding ecosystem restoration to other federal projects? Should all large-scale water projects (e.g., locks, dams, and levees) have an ecosystem restoration component? In addition to their ecosystems, rivers are resources that may be used for multiple purposes such as hydro power, navigation, flood control, recreation, and water supply. While many facilities, such as dams,[66] are managed for multiple purposes, agencies have been directed to construct and operate a number of federal projects for single purposes. Should all federal projects be managed for multiple purposes? Linking ecosystem restoration and navigation, as with any multi-purpose designation, is ultimately a policy question of how Congress wants federal agencies to manage public resources.

CONCLUSION

The Army Corps of Engineers has released a final feasibility report and Chief's Report recommending that Congress authorize a 15-year, initial increment of ecosystem restoration measures as part of a combined 50-year investment and management framework for UMR-IWW navigation and UMRS restoration. Authorization of UMRS restoration poses policy questions for decision makers, such as: What level of restoration should be authorized, and at what cost? What should be the federal responsibility for UMRS restoration investments? Congress is being asked to answer these questions in the context of interest in and debate over navigation expansion on the UMR-IWW. The answers that Congress may provide are likely to be viewed as precedent setting for other large-scale restoration efforts, especially efforts for ecosystem restoration of other inland waterways and rivers.

An additional challenge is the uncertainty of what would be achieved through UMRS restoration investments. This uncertainty comes from multiple sources: ecosystem restoration is a young science; the Corps' plan only addresses some of the stressors causing ecosystem decline; and restoration implementation depends on available appropriations. The issue for policymakers is further complicated because analytic tools to assist in decision-making for restoration projects are less robust than for other Corps projects that use benefit-cost analysis. The Corps has recognized these challenges in its feasibility report. In response, the agency recommends an adaptive management and implementation strategy for restoration; however, some observers see adaptive management as contributing another element of uncertainty and risk. Congress may weigh these risks when considering the level of ecosystem restoration and federal investment for the UMRS, if it wants to make these restoration investments in conjunction with navigation expansion, or separately, and what role it wants during implementation and funding.

REFERENCES

[1] The UMRS includes the Upper Mississippi River from Minneapolis, Minnesota, to Cairo, Illinois (854 river miles); the Illinois Waterway from Chicago to Grafton, Illinois (327 river miles); and navigable portions of the Minnesota (15 river miles), St. Croix (24 river miles), Black (1 river mile), and Kaskaskia River (36 river miles).

[2] Hereafter referred to as Corps, *Final Feasibility Report and PEIS.* Available at [http:// www2.mvr.usace.army.mil/umr-iwwsns/documents/Main_Report_Final.pdf].

[3] For more information on the Corps' proposal for navigation improvements, see CRS Report RL32470, *Upper Mississippi River-Illinois Waterway Navigation Expansion: An Agricultural Transportation and Environmental Context,* coordinated by Randy Schnepf.

[4] For a discussion of Corps reform, see CRS Issue Brief IB10133, *Water Resources Development Act: Army Corps of Engineers Authorization Issues in the 109th Congress,* coordinated by Nicole T. Carter.

[5] The Department of Defense requested, in February 2000, that the National Research Council independently review the Corps' ongoing feasibility study. The National Academy of Sciences completed its report in 2001. National Academy of Sciences, *Inland Navigation System Planning: The Upper Mississippi River-Illinois Waterway* (Washington, 2001).

[6] National Research Council, *Review of the U.S. Army Corps of Engineers Upper Mississippi-Illinois Waterway Restructured Study:*

Interim Report (Washington: National Academy Press, December 2003).

[7] The prepublication version of the October 2004 report, *Review of the U.S. Army Corps of Engineers Restructured Upper Mississippi River-Illinois Waterway Feasibility Study: Second Report* is available at [http://books.nap.edu/catalog/11109.html]. Hereafter referred to as October 2004 NRC report.

[8] Corps, *Final Feasibility Report and PEIS,* p. 96; Gary R. Clark, Upper Mississippi River Basin Association (UMRBA), *Testimony on Upper Mississippi River and Illinois River Recommendations for Navigation Improvements and Ecosystem Restoration before the Subcommittee on Water Resources and Environment Committee on Transportation and Infrastructure U.S. House of Representatives* (June 24, 2004). Hereafter referred to as Upper Mississippi River Basin Association June 24, 2004 testimony. The UMRBA is an interstate organization of governor-appointed representatives from all five basin states to help coordinate the states' river-related programs and policies and work with federal agencies that have river responsibilities.

[9] U.S. Department of the Interior, Geological Survey, *Ecological Status and Trends of the Upper Mississippi River System 1998.* p. 12-2. Hereafter referred to as USGS, *Status and Trends 1998.*

[10] Ibid., p. 12-2.

[11] Corps, *Final Feasibility Report and PEIS,* p. 470.

[12] A recreational visit is defined as one person visiting for one day. One person visiting for two days, or two people visiting for one day each, would equal two recreational visits.

[13] Corps, *Final Feasibility Report and PEIS*, p. 146-147.

[14] Ibid., p. 147. This includes revenue from people who hunt, fish, boat, sightsee, or otherwise visit the river and communities.

[15] Upper Mississippi River Wildlife and Fish Refuge Act of June, 1924 Ch. 346 (16 U.S.C. 721-731) The UMRS also includes four other fish and wildlife refuges. These are the Mark Twain, Trempealeau, Minnesota Valley, and Illinois River National Wildlife Refuges. Overall, the refuges cover 297,000 acres.

[16] Navigation requires elevated water levels during dry seasons, so sediment deposited in shallow backwater and side channels is not compacted by exposure to air. This results in the sediment being easily resuspended into the water column, where it reduces light penetration essential for plant growth. Less vegetation reduces aquatic insects, fish, waterfowl, and other animals.

[17] Corps, *Final Feasibility Report and PEIS,* p. 100.

[18] "Backwaters — A small, generally shallow body of water attached to the main channel, with little or no current of its own; shallow, slow-moving water associated with a river but outside the river's main channel." Ibid., 611.

[19] Ibid., p. 106.

[20] USGS, *Status and Trends 1998*, p. 8-8.

[21] Ibid., p. 11-1.

[22] Ibid., p. 12-4.

[23] Ibid., p. 7-17.

[24] Ibid., p. 12-5.

[25] The Corps provides before and after pictures for one of its EMP projects in Corps, *Final Feasibility Report and PEIS,* p.8.

[26] U.S. Army Corps of Engineers, Rock Island District. *2004 Report to Congress: Upper Mississippi River System Environmental Management Program.*

[27] Corps, *Final Feasibility Report and PEIS,* p. 104.

[28] Upper Mississippi River Conservation Committee, *Facing the Threat: An Ecosystem Management Strategy for the Upper Mississippi River* (1993).

[29] The $200 million for mitigation of incremental environmental damage associated with navigation improvements is included in the navigation plan, not the restoration plan.

[30] The USGS states that habitat is critical because "the diversity and abundance of species found in the river depends on the diversity and abundance of habitat." USGS, *Status and Trends 1998,* p. 7-2. The plan places a particular emphasis on backwater habitat, which is one of the primary types of habitat being lost.

[31] Navigation is currently the only authorized purpose of the UMR-IWW.

[32] Corps, *Final Feasibility Report and PEIS*, p. 491.

[33] Part of the Corps definition of adaptive management is: An approach to natural resources management that acknowledges the risk and uncertainty of ecosystem restoration and allows for modification of restoration measures to optimize performance. The process of implementing policy decisions as scientifically driven management experiments that test predictions and assumptions in management plans, using the resulting information to improve the plans. (sic) (Ibid., p. 611)

[34] Ibid., p. 512.

[35] Ibid., p. 491.
[36] Upper Mississippi River Basin Association June 24, 2004 testimony.
[37] Christopher J. Brescia, Midwest Area River Coalition 2000 (MARC 2000), *Testimony before the House Transportation and Infrastructure Subcommittee on Water Resources and Environment*, June 24, 2004.
[38] Corps, *Final Feasibility Report and PEIS,* p. 482 and 485.
[39] Ibid., p. 512.
[40] October 2004 NRC report, p. 8.
[41] Ibid., 56.
[42] The Corps focused its alternatives analysis on 50-year plans. Analyses of the alternative plans (A, B, C, and E) do not include a discrete discussion of the first 15-year increment. The Corps also examined multiple options for navigation improvements; these are not discussed in this report.
[43] Corps, *Final Feasibility Report and PEIS,* p. 183.
[44] These projects correspond to the following acreage for alternatives B through D: (B) 1,000, (C) 16,000, (D) 105,500, and (E) 251,500.
[45] The Corps describes "acres of influence" as "the area positively affected by the restoration measure" (ibid., p. viii). It is estimated using data gained from already implemented restoration measures, primarily EMP projects. The October 2004 NRC report (p. 8) is critical of the acres of influence metric as poorly correlated with ecological outcomes.
[46] Ibid., p. 232.
[47] Ibid., pp. 469 and x.
[48] Corps navigation projects are evaluated using benefit-cost analyses, in which benefits are monetized, thus facilitating comparison across projects. This analysis is not used for restoration projects because computing the economic value of restoration benefits is difficult.
[49] Corps, *Final Feasibility Report and PEIS*, p. 515.
[50] Ibid., p. 515.
[51] Ibid., p. 515.
[52] Ibid., p. 515.
[53] Ibid., pp. 511-512.
[54] Ibid., p. 477.
[55] Ibid., pp. 512-513.
[56] These estimates were updated by Congressional Research Service based on data provided in the U.S. Dept. of the Interior, U.S. Fish and Wildlife Service. *Draft Supplement to the April 2002 Draft Fish and*

Wildlife Coordination Act Report for the Upper Mississippi and Illinois River System Navigation Feasibility Study (April 2004).

[57] M. Reuss, *Reshaping National Water Politics: The Emergence of the Water Resources Development Act of 1986* (Alexandria, VA: U.S. Army Corps of Engineers, Institute for Water Resources, Oct. 1991).

[58] Ibid., p. 199.

[59] The October 2004 NRC report (p. 52) was critical of using a market test for UMRS investments because of the role of the UMR-IWW navigation project in ecosystem decline and because the benefits of restoration investment may not be local.

[60] Corps, *Final Feasibility Report and PEIS*, p. QM-5.

[61] Ibid., p. QM-5.

[62] This interest in natural river processes and floodplain connectivity is linked to another criticism made by the NRC; the October 2004 NRC report (p. 8) states that ... proposed restoration measures represent an impressive range and number of candidate actions. The assembly of those measures into restoration alternatives, however, is not adequately grounded in principles and theories of large river floodplain science and restoration.

[63] Ibid., pp. 2-3. The October 2004 NRC report also questions if the Corps' assumption that the navigation season and 9-foot channel depth will remain unchanged is appropriate, and if this assumption implicitly gives navigation a superior position to other river uses (ibid., pp. 19-20).

[64] These organizations do not necessarily support the Corps entire navigation proposal. They tend to oppose lock expansion but support small-scale measures.

[65] For more information on current legislation, see CRS Report RL32574, *Upper Mississippi River-Illinois Waterway Investments: Proposed Authorization Legislation in the 108th Congress*, by Nicole T. Carter and Kyna Powers.

[66] Most federal dams are managed for multiple purposes. Furthermore, licenses issued by the Federal Energy Regulatory Commission for non-federal dams often contain provisions aimed at retaining or enhancing the river's recreational, ecological, or tribal benefits.

INDEX

A

adaptability, 36
affect, 8
aging, 25
alternative, 15, 26, 32, 33, 36, 37, 38, 39, 47
alternatives, 7, 11, 15, 35, 36, 37, 47, 48
alters, viii, 23
amendments, 21
animals, 15, 29, 45
assessment, 4, 7
assumptions, 46
attacks, 3, 6
authority, 3, 8, 9, 11, 12, 20, 33, 38

B

backwaters, viii, 23, 28, 29
birds, 21, 29, 30, 31
body, 15, 46
budget deficit, 41

C

channels, viii, 23, 28, 29, 45
cluster, 6
commitment, 33, 41
community, 4, 13, 42
compensation, 10
competition, 4
complexity, 29
components, 11, 37
computing, 47
conduct, 3, 19
conflict, vii, 1
connectivity, 36, 38, 48
conservation, vii, 2, 4, 18
construction, 4, 5, 6, 8, 11, 12, 13, 14, 15, 18, 19, 28, 37, 38, 41
contamination, 28
context, 26, 33, 35, 41, 42, 43
control, vii, 1, 3, 5, 12, 37, 43
coping, 34
cost effectiveness, 36, 37
costs, 4, 5, 6, 9, 10, 11, 12, 14, 15, 16, 32, 36, 37, 40
criticism, 7, 24, 27, 48
customers, 5

D

damage, 40, 41, 42, 46
data collection, 34
death, 7
decision makers, 43
decisions, 39, 46
definition, 46
degradation, 28, 31, 34, 40, 41, 42

delivery, 4
demand, vii, 1, 5
Department of Defense, 3, 44
Department of the Interior, 15
desire, 39
differentiation, 35
dissolved oxygen, 29
distribution, 28, 31, 40
diversity, 32, 36, 46
dominance, 40, 41
draft, 24, 27
drainage, 14
drought, 2, 7, 20, 21
drying, 29

E

economic assistance, 7
economic development, 36
ecosystem restoration, 2, 24, 25, 26, 27, 28, 31, 32, 33, 34, 36, 37, 38, 39, 40, 41, 42, 43, 46
ecosystems, 24, 40, 43
enthusiasm, 7
environment, 11, 27
environmental degradation, 5
environmental effects, vii, 4, 9, 23, 24
environmental impact, 27
Environmental Protection Agency, 34
erosion, 5
Everglades, 5, 41
evidence, 27
exposure, 45
extinction, 7

F

farm land, 4
farmers, 5, 7, 8
farmland, 3
fear, 9, 13, 41
financing, 12, 40, 41
fish, viii, 2, 7, 8, 9, 11, 14, 20, 23, 29, 30, 31, 32, 35, 37, 38, 45
fisheries, 2, 4, 12
fishing, 29
flexibility, 33, 34
flood, vii, 1, 3, 12, 37, 41, 42, 43
fluctuations, 36
food, 2, 12
freshwater, 15, 29
funding, vii, 2, 6, 8, 10, 12, 13, 14, 41, 43, 44

G

generation, vii, 1, 3
goals, 39
goods and services, 33, 36
governance, 11
government, vii, 1, 3, 5, 32, 39
grants, 21
groundwater, 13, 14
groups, 4, 11, 27, 31, 42
growth, viii, 23, 28, 34, 45
Gulf of Mexico, 28

H

habitat, viii, 2, 4, 7, 11, 15, 23, 29, 31, 32, 35, 37, 38, 46
hands, 9
harm, 32
Hawaii, 17, 21
health, 31, 32
hunting, 29
hydroelectric power, 33

I

implementation, 2, 10, 11, 12, 13, 20, 25, 34, 35, 38, 44
incentives, 18
indicators, 31
industry, 34

influence, 32, 36, 37, 47
infrastructure, 25, 28, 29, 41
initiation, 34
insects, 45
integration, 34
integrity, 34
intent, 3
interest, 4, 12, 43, 48
intervention, 42
investment, 24, 36, 40, 43, 44, 48

J

jobs, 29
justification, 40

K

knowledge, 38

L

lakes, 15
land, 8, 9, 28, 37, 38, 40, 41
land acquisition, 37, 38
land use, 41
land-use, 28
language, 6, 9, 10, 11
laws, 3, 4, 9, 10
learning, 34
legislation, 2, 3, 5, 6, 8, 9, 10, 12, 13, 24, 43, 48
levees, 28, 43
liability, 10
licenses, 48
limitation, 4
linkage, 26, 27
livestock, 33
Louisiana, 41

M

management, vii, 1, 2, 4, 5, 7, 8, 9, 25, 27, 28, 32, 33, 34, 35, 37, 38, 41, 42, 43, 44, 46
mandates, 5
market, vii, 2, 40, 48
measures, 25, 27, 32, 33, 35, 36, 38, 41, 43, 46, 47, 48
Mexico, 12, 19
migration, 38
military, 18
Mississippi River, v, vii, 23, 24, 28, 29, 30, 31, 33, 42, 44, 45, 46, 47, 48
modeling, 34
money, 15, 34
monitoring, 31, 34, 35
motivation, 40
movement, viii, 23, 28
multiple factors, 28

N

National Research Council, 8, 27, 44
natural resources, 46
navigation system, vii, 23, 24, 25, 28, 38, 39, 40, 42
needs, vii, 1, 4, 10, 18, 27
negotiating, 9
North America, 29

O

obligation, 9
optimization, 37
organization, 45
organizations, 15, 33, 34, 36, 38, 40, 41, 42, 48
orientation, 29
ownership, 8, 9, 40

P

Pacific, 5, 21
partition, 10
partnership, 19
perspective, 12
planning, 4, 7, 19, 38
plants, 15, 29
pools, 29
population, vii, 1, 7
ports, 28
power, vii, 1, 3, 43
power plants, 3
precipitation, 4
preparedness, 21
pricing policies, 4
producers, 7, 25
program, 2, 5, 6, 10, 11, 13, 14, 16, 31, 34
public resources, 43

R

range, 8, 37, 48
recognition, 34
recovery, 8
recreation, vii, 1, 4, 14, 29, 43
recycling, 2, 13, 14, 17, 21
reduction, 41, 42
rehabilitation, 20, 31, 39
relationship, 39
resolution, 11
resource management, 8
resources, 4, 21, 34, 43
responsibility, 3, 24, 37, 40, 43
restored ecosystem, 39
revenue, 45
rights, 2, 7, 20
risk, 33, 44, 46
river systems, vii, 1
rural areas, 12

S

sales, 15
salinity, 15
savings, 33
scarcity, 7
security, 3, 6
sediment, viii, 23, 28, 29, 42, 45
sedimentation, 30, 41
selecting, 35
Senate, 2, 11, 13, 17, 18, 19, 20, 21
series, 29
services, 14, 31, 40
shape, 42
sharing, 37, 40
sites, 35
species, vii, 1, 7, 9, 15, 23, 28, 29, 30, 31, 32, 38, 46
sports, 5, 29
stages, 12, 31
stakeholders, 5, 34
storage, vii, 2, 3, 11, 12, 19
stressors, 27, 41, 42, 43
suppliers, 5
supply, vii, 1, 2, 3, 5, 8, 11, 12, 13, 14, 19, 33, 43
symptoms, 41
systems, 3, 13

T

targets, 41
technology, 21
temperature, 29
threshold, 43
time, 4, 5, 6, 9, 10, 32, 34, 35, 38
time frame, 38
training, 28
transactions, 9
transport, 29, 42
transportation, vii, 23, 25, 28
tribes, 7

U

U.S. Geological Survey, 29
uncertainty, 34, 43, 46
United States, 21, 31

values, vii, 1, 40
vegetation, 45

wastewater, 13, 14, 21
water, vii, 1, 2, 3, 4, 5, 6, 7, 8, 9, 10, 11, 12, 13, 14, 15, 17, 18, 19, 20, 21, 23, 28, 29, 32, 33, 36, 37, 38, 41, 42, 43, 45, 46
water policy, 4, 5
water quality, 11, 13, 19, 28, 29, 41, 42
water resources, vii, 1, 4, 17, 21
water supplies, vii, 1, 5, 11, 14
watershed, 27, 28, 41, 42
waterways, 25, 43
wetlands, viii, 15, 23, 28, 29, 41
wildlife, 2, 4, 9, 11, 14, 29, 45
winter, 31
work, 34, 38, 45